Teatime

TALES & RHYMES

THE METROPOLITAN MUSEUM OF ART

BARNES
&NOBLE
BOOKS
NEW YORK

All of the works of art reproduced in this book are from the collections of The Metropolitan Museum of Art.

BACK COVER AND ENDPAPERS: English, 19th century. Engraved-roller print on cotton.
COVER: Kate Greenaway, British, 1846–1901. Illustration from *Under the Window*, 1878.
TITLE PAGE: Edmund Evans, British, 1826–1905, after Kate Greenaway, British, 1846–1901.
Afternoon Tea, illustration from *The Girl's Own Annual*, 1886–87.
INTRODUCTION: Kate Greenaway, British, 1846–1901.
Illustration from *Little Anne and Other Poems*, 1882.

Published by The Metropolitan Museum of Art, New York, and Barnes & Noble, Inc., 122 Fifth Avenue, New York, NY 10011.

Copyright © 2004 by The Metropolitan Museum of Art

First Edition
Printed and manufactured in China
12 11 10 09 08 07 06 05 04 03   5 4 3 2 1

Produced by the Department of Special Publications, The Metropolitan Museum of Art:
Robie Rogge, Publishing Manager; Judith Cressy, Project Editor; Anna Raff, Designer; Gillian Moran, Production Associate.

All photography by The Metropolitan Museum of Art Photograph Studio

ISBN 1-58839-041-1 (MMA)
ISBN 0-7607-4498-X (B&N)

$\mathcal{C}$hildren have enjoyed their own tea parties since at least
the early nineteenth century, when the vogue for afternoon
tea began. Artists and writers, most of them British, have
memorialized these childhood occasions for nearly as long.
Some of their works—prints and children's book illustrations
from the Museum's collections, and poetry and prose from
many sources—are gathered into this little book. Cats, dogs,
the Mad Hatter, and even Beauty and the Beast have tea along
with the children on these pages. We hope they will inspire
many memorable tea parties yet to come.

Judith Cressy

Polly, Put the Kettle On

Polly, put the kettle on,
Polly, put the kettle on,
Polly, put the kettle on,
We'll all have tea.

Sukey, take it off again,
Sukey, take it off again,
Sukey, take it off again,
They're all gone away.

Mother Goose (Anonymous),
British, 18th century

Kate Greenaway, British, 1846–1901. Illustration from *Mother Goose, or The Old Nursery Rhymes*, 1881

Garden Tea

Who wouldn't like to drink afternoon tea
Out in the garden just like me?
With the song of a bird, and the hum of a bee,
And the sunflowers looking all eyes to see.

Traditional

American, 1886. *Tea Party*, advertisement for the Great Atlantic and Pacific Tea Company

Prince Finikin

Prince Finikin and his mamma,
  Sat sipping their bohea;
"Good gracious!" said his Highness, "why,
  What girl is this I see?

"Most certainly it cannot be
  A native of our town;"
And he turned him round to his mamma,
  Who set her teacup down.

But Dolly simply looked at them,
  She did not speak a word;
"She has no voice!" said Finikin;
"It's really quite absurd."

Kate Greenaway, British, 1846–1901. Illustration from *Under the Window*, 1878

Then Finikin's mamma observed,
"Dear Prince, it seems to me,
She looks as if she'd like to drink
A cup of my bohea."

So Finikin poured out her tea,
And gave her currant pie;
Then Finikin said, "Dear mamma,
What a kind prince am I."

Kate Greenaway, British, 1846–1901

The Cats Have Come to Tea

What did she see—oh, what did she see,
As she stood leaning against the tree?
Why all the cats had come to tea.

What a fine turn out—from round about,
All the houses had let them out,
And here they were with scamper and shout.

"Mew—mew—mew!" was all they could say,
And, "We hope we find you well to-day."

Oh, what should she do—oh, what should she do?
What a lot of milk they would get through;
For here they were with "Mew—mew—mew!"

She didn't know—oh, she didn't know,
If bread and butter they'd like or no;
They might want little mice, oh! oh! oh!

Dear me—oh, dear me,
All the cats had come to tea.

Kate Greenaway, British, 1846–1901

August Bang, Danish, 19th century. Illustration from *Aftengildet hos Frøken Maw-Miawski*

A Mad Tea Party

There was a table set out under a tree in front of the house, and the March Hare and the Hatter were having tea at it: a Dormouse was sitting between them, fast asleep, and the other two were using it as a cushion, resting their elbows on it, and talking over its head. "Very uncomfortable for the Dormouse," thought Alice; "only as it's asleep, I suppose it doesn't mind."

The table was a large one, but the three were all crowded together at one corner of it. "No room! No room!" they cried out when they saw Alice coming. "There's *plenty* of room!" said Alice indignantly, and she sat down in a large arm-chair at one end of the table.

Lewis Carroll, British, 1832–1898

Arthur Rackham, British, 1867–1939. Illustration from *Alice's Adventures in Wonderland*, 1907

Walter Crane, British, 1845–1915.
Illustration from *Beauty and the Beast*

My Party

I had a little tea party, this afternoon at three.
'Twas very small, three guests in all, I, Myself, and Me.
Myself ate up the sandwiches, while I drank up the tea.
'Twas also I who ate the pie and passed the cake to Me!

Traditional

American, ca. 1886. *Take Sugar*, advertisement for the Great Atlantic and Pacific Tea Company

Merry Phillis

You see, merry Phillis, that dear little maid,
Has invited Belinda to tea;
Her nice little garden is shaded by trees—
What pleasanter place could there be?

There's a cake full of plums, there are strawberries too,
And the table is set on the green;
I'm fond of a carpet all daisies and grass—
Could a prettier picture be seen?

Kate Greenaway, British, 1846–1901

Kate Greenaway, British, 1846–1901. Illustration from *Under the Window*, 1878

Cross Patch

Cross Patch, draw the latch,
Sit by the fire and spin;
Take a cup and drink it up,
Then call your neighbors in.

Mother Goose (Anonymous),
British, 18th century

Frederick Richardson, American, 1862–1937. Illustration from *Mother Goose*, 1915

The Tea Party

In the pleasant green garden
We sat down to tea;
"Do you take sugar?" and
"Do you take milk?"
She'd got a new gown on—
A smart one of silk.
We all were so happy
As happy could be,
On that bright summer's day
When she asked us to tea.

Kate Greenaway, British, 1846–1901

François David Soiron, b. Switzerland, active in Britain 1764–after 1793.
After George Morland, British, 1763–1804. *A Tea Garden*, stipple and engraving, 1793

A Cup of Tea

When the world is all at odds
And the mind is all at sea
Then cease the useless tedium
And brew a cup of tea.
There is magic in its fragrance,
There is solace in its taste;
And the laden moments vanish
Somehow into space.
And the world becomes a lovely thing!
There's beauty as you'll see;
All because you briefly stopped
To brew a cup of tea.

Traditional

American, 1886. *The Fortune Teller*, advertisement for the Great Atlantic and Pacific Tea Company

Twinkle, Twinkle

Twinkle, twinkle, little bat!
How I wonder what you're at!
Up above the world you fly,
Like a tea-tray in the sky.

Lewis Carroll,
British, 1832–1898

Sir John Tenniel, British, 1820–1914. Illustration from *Alice's Adventures in Wonderland,* 1866

You Are Going Out to Tea

You are going out to tea today,
So mind how you behave;
Let all accounts I have of you
Be pleasant ones, I crave.

Say "If you please," and "Thank you, Nurse;"
Come home at eight o'clock;
And, Fanny, pray be careful that
You do not tear your frock.

Now, mind your manners, children five,
Attend to what I say;
And then, perhaps, I'll let you go
Again another day.

Kate Greenaway, British, 1846–1901

Kate Greenaway, British, 1846–1901. Illustration from *Under the Window*, 1878

Illustration Credits

BACK COVER AND ENDPAPERS: Gift of William Sloane Coffin, 1926   26.265.127. COVER AND PAGE 21: Museum Accession; transferred from the Library, 1921   21.36.94. TITLE PAGE: Gift of Mrs. John Barry Ryan, 1983   1983.1223.20. INTRODUCTION: Gift of Mrs. John Barry Ryan, 1983   1983.1223.2. PAGE 4: Museum Accession; transferred from the Library, 1921   21.36.98. PAGE 7: The Jefferson R. Burdick Collection, Gift of Jefferson R. Burdick [Album 19]. PAGE 8: Museum Accession; transferred from the Library, 1921   21.36.94. PAGE 13: Gift of Lincoln Kirstein, 1970   1970.565.137. PAGE 14: Gift of Fairchild Bowler, 1965   65.518.35. PAGES 16–17: The Elisha Whittelsey Collection, The Elisha Whittelsey Fund, 1972   1972.655.1. PAGE 18: The Jefferson R. Burdick Collection, Gift of Jefferson R. Burdick [Album 19]. PAGE 22: Gift of Estate of Jane Erdman Whitney, 1986   1986.1145.21. PAGE 25: Gift of Dr. Bruce B. Grynbaum, in memory of his parents, Gertrude and Maurycy Grynbaum, 1991   1991.1335.2. PAGE 26: The Jefferson R. Burdick Collection, Gift of Jefferson R. Burdick [Album 19]. PAGE 29: Gift of Miss Lilian Green, 1957   57.621.1. PAGE 30: Museum Accession; transferred from the Library, 1921   21.36.94.